Going places

by Jayne Garner

AXIS education

Acknowledgements

Photographs:

Page 3 Travel Agent © Midcounties Co-op Travel

Actors: Stephenson Ardern-Sodje and Rachel Barton

First published in Great Britain by Axis Education Ltd

ISBN 978-1-86418-125-2

Axis Education
PO Box 459
Shrewsbury
SY4 4WZ

Email: enquiries@axiseducation.co.uk

www.axiseducation.co.uk

Tom and Kim have got some time off.
They want to go on holiday.

Where shall they go?

Kim thinks a trip to Paris would be good.

But Tom says he does not like French food.

Tom thinks a camping trip would be good.

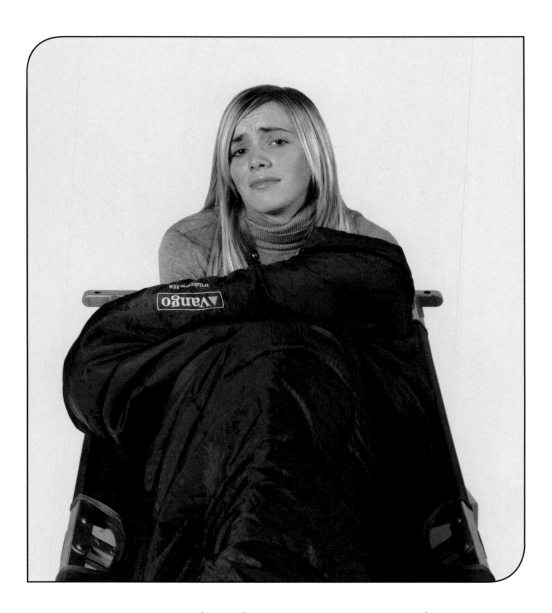

But Kim says she does not want to kip in a tent.

Kim thinks a trip to Australia would be good.

But Tom says it will cost too much.

Tom thinks a trip to Jamaica would be good.

But Kim says she does not want to stay with Tom's family.

Kim thinks a trip to Scotland would be good.

But Tom says he wants to go somewhere hotter.

Tom thinks a trip to Ibiza would be good.

But Kim says she is fed up with going to clubs.

Kim thinks a trip to London would be good.

But Tom says it will be too busy. He wants
to relax.

Tom thinks a trip to Egypt would be good.

But Kim says she does not like old things.

Kim thinks a skiing trip would be good.

But Tom says Kim does not listen. He has told her he does not like the cold.

We can not find a holiday we both like.
What shall we do?

Let's not go on holiday. Let's go on day trips!